The Baa Day

Written by
Jill Atkins

Illustrated by
Cristina Martin

Ransom

The quick fox ran up the hill.

He ran to his den.

He had a hen in his sack.

The vixen sat in the den.

She had six cubs.

5

The hen fell in the mud.

It got up and ran off.

The hen met a big, fat bug on the hill.

Did the big, fat bug buzz at the hen?

Yes, it did.

9

Did the hen zap
the big, fat bug?

No, she did not.

But the fox did zap the bug.

11

Did the six cubs get the bug?

Yes.

But the bug is bad. Yuk!